BIBLE LESSONS

Student Workbook

52 Bible Lessons
Bible Introduction for Children
Ages 6-12

How to use this workbook:

This book was designed to introduce children to the Bible. It is centered on children 6-12 years old. The Student Workbook can be used as a Sunday School curriculum, weekly church activity, or as a home school curriculum. This book is designed for any Christian denomination. See page 3 for the recommended order for lessons if you are teaching this weekly. Each year, this supplement will be available and updated. The date of Easter changes and so the calendar and lessons need to changed every year.

The book has an easy to follow format. Each lesson begins with a "Warm-up" designed to get children focused on the lesson, but allows late-comers a chance to catch up. Next is a "Lesson" that is planned for approximately 20 minutes. During this time children will look up verses in their Bible. Encouraging them to really dig into their Bible and learn how it is laid-out. The lesson is followed by a "Snack". The snack is optional and can be as elaborate or simple as you choose. Ideas for snacks that relate to the lesson are provided each week; however, a standard simple snack is a great option. Each lesson is concluded with an "Activity", game, or craft that relates to the lesson.

This book is available as a downloadable eBook or a printed workbook. It is okay to reproduce the downloadable eBook multiple times for one church or household. It is not okay to sell this as your own product or to share it with more than one church/building. You may print this in either black or white or color (it looks great in both). The pre-printed version is available in color or black and white. If you are printing it yourself, I suggest that you print the entire workbook and put the pages into a paper folder with brads or a small 1/2 inch 3-ring binder. You will need a copy of the Teacher Workbook. You may purchase the Teacher Workbook at **www.52BibleLessons.com.**

This curriculum works best if you use both the Teacher Workbook and Student Workbook together. Some lessons will be very difficult to complete if you only have the Teacher Workbook.

By His Grace,

Lorraine Gilbert. Author

Brief Outline of Lessons 1-52

Lesson	Topic	Page(s)
1	Parents go to Children's Sunday School/Activity	4
2	Bible Presentation/Blessing of the Backpacks	5-6
3	Bible Breakdown	7
4	Overview of the Old and New Testament	8-9
5	Preparation for Advent (Before Advent)	10-11
6	Prophecies about the Birth of Jesus (Christmas 1)	12
7	Mary and Joseph (Christmas 2)	13
8	Travel (Christmas 3)	14
9	Birth of Jesus (Christmas 4)	15
10	The Three Kings (After Christmas)	16
11	Ash Wednesday and Lent	17
12	Holy Week	18
13	Palm Sunday	19
14	Easter	20
15	Ascension	21
16	Pentecost	22
17	Mother's Day	23
18	Father's Day	24
19	Famous Children in the Bible	25
20	Where Jesus Traveled	26
21	Celebration	27
22	Leap Year– Help for Prayers	28
23	Genesis	29
24	Exodus	30
25	Leviticus & Numbers	31
26	Deuteronomy	32
27	Joshua, Judges, and Ruth	33

Lesson	Topic	Page(s)
28	1 Samuel & 2 Samuel	34
29	Kings & Chronicles	35
30	Ezra, Nehemiah, and Esther	36
31	Job	37
32	Psalms	38
33	Proverbs	39-40
34	Ecclesiastes & Song of Solomon	41
35	Isaiah, Jeremiah, Lamentations , & Ezekiel	42
36	Daniel, Hosea, Joel, & Amos	43
37	Obadiah, Jonah, Micah, Nahum, & Habakkuk	44
38	Zephaniah, Haggai, Zechariah, & Malachi	45
39	Matthew Part 1	46
40	Matthew Part 2	47
41	Mark	48
42	Luke	49
43	John	50
44	Acts, Part 1	51
45	Acts, Part 2	52
46	Romans	53
47	Corinthians	54
48	Galatians, Ephesians, Philippians, & Colossians	55
49	Thessalonians & Timothy	56
50	Titus, Philemon, & Hebrews	57
51	James & Peter	58
52	Three books of John & Jude	59
53	Revelation	60

Craft:

On a separate piece of paper, draw a picture about your family. Name the people that live in your house and your pets. Include things you love; like your favorite place to sit, your favorite toy, and what you like best about being in your home. Make sure you write your name on the sheet so we may display it!

BIBLE LESSONS

[9] Our Father in __ __ __ __ __ __, hallowed be your name,
[10] your __ __ __ __ __ __ __ come, your will be __ __ __ __,

On __ __ __ __ __ as it is in heaven.

[11] Give us today our daily __ __ __ __ __.

[12] And forgive us our __ __ __ __ __,

as we also have __ __ __ __ __ __ __ __ our debtors.

[13] and lead us not into temptation,

but deliver us from the evil one.

Matthew 6: 9-13

Handwrite your church's version of The Lord's Prayer below in your best handwriting.

_____

_____

_____

_____

_____

_____

_____

Lesson 2: Bible Presentation/Blessing of the Back-

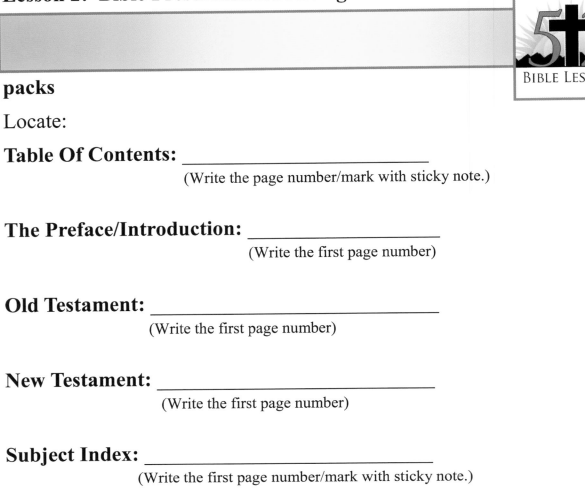

packs

Locate:

Table Of Contents: _____

(Write the page number/mark with sticky note.)

The Preface/Introduction: _____

(Write the first page number)

Old Testament: _____

(Write the first page number)

New Testament: _____

(Write the first page number)

Subject Index: _____

(Write the first page number/mark with sticky note.)

Dictionary/Concordance: _____

(Write the first page number/mark with sticky note.)

Maps: _____

(Write the first page number/mark with sticky note.)

Lesson 3: Bible Breakdown

BIBLE LESSONS

Locate:

Genesis (First book of Law): _____

(Write the page number/mark with a sticky note)

Joshua (First book of History): _____

(Write the page number/mark with a sticky note)

Job (First book of Poetry): _____

(Write the page number/mark with a sticky note

Isaiah (First book of Prophets): _____

(Write the page number/mark with a sticky note)

Matthew (First book of Gospels): _____

(Write the page number/mark with sticky note)

Romans (First book of Letters): _____

(Write the page number/mark with sticky note)

Revelation (Book of Prophecy): _____

(Write the page number/mark with sticky note)

Lesson 4: Overview of the Old and New Testament

Fill in the missing books, by using the "Table of Contents".

Color the books
Law: Red
History: Yellow
Poetry: Green
Prophets: Orange
Gospels: Blue
Letters: Purple
Prophecy: Light Purple

Old Testament

Law: Genesis, Leviticus, Deuteronomy

History: Joshua, Judges, 1 Samuel, 2 Samuel, 1 Kings, 1 Chronicles, 2 Chronicles, Ezra, Esther

Poetry: Job, Ecclesiastes, Song of Solomon

Prophets: Isaiah, Jeremiah, Lamentations, Ezekiel, Hosea, Joel, Obadiah, Micah, Nahum, Habakkuk, Haggai, Zechariah, Malachi

New Testament

Gospels: Matthew, John

History: Acts

Letters: Romans, 1 Corinthians, 2 Corinthians, Ephesians, Philippians, 1 Thessalonians, 2 Thessalonians, 1 Timothy, Titus, Philemon, James, 1 Peter, 2 Peter, 1 John, 2 John, Jude

Prophecy: Revelation

Lesson 4: Overview of the Old and New Testament

How many books?

Books of Law: _____

Books of Old Testament History: _____

Books of Poetry: _____

Books of Prophets: _____

Books of Gospels: _____

Books of New Testament History: _____

Books of Letters: _____

Book of Prophecy: _____

Books of Old Testament: _____

Books of New Testament: _____

Total number of books in the Bible: _____

Color the Advent candles.

Lesson 5: Preparation for Advent

Craft for parents

Put on a paint smock or a large t-shirt to protect your clothes.

1.) Write your name on the back of the paper or canvas board you are given.

2.) Tape the shape of a cross to the paper or canvas board you are given.

3.) Choose two paint colors provided by your teacher and swirl them together over your canvas board. Swirl on top of the tape and all over the white areas of your canvas.

4.) Allow the paint to dry.

5.) Carefully remove the tape when dry. You will have a beautiful painting suitable for framing. This is an excellent Christmas gift for someone you love.

Lesson 6: Prophecies about the Birth of Jesus

You will be making an Angel Ornament for the Christmas tree.

Supplies: 5 Round Coffee Filters
Clear Tape
1 Chenille stem pipe cleaner

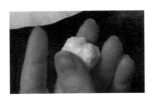

Take one coffee filter and scrunch it up into a ball.

Cover the scrunched coffee filter with another coffee filter. Twist the second coffee filter around the scrunched coffee filter to form a head.

Fold another coffee filter in half and wrap it around the neck of the assembled head. Tape folded coffee filter to the back of the head, making a dress. Take another folded coffee filter and repeat this so that the dress is fuller.

Take the 5th coffee filter, fold it in half and scrunch it in the center. Wrap the chenille stem around in the center and twist the stem. Attach the wings to the neck of the angel by wrapping the loose ends of the chenille stem around the neck of the angel. Twist the stem around the back of the angel and then loop the ends of the angel together.

Twist and mold the looped end of the chenille stem to form a halo or to use it to hang the angel to the tree. If you are using the stem as a halo, you can use paper clips or fishing line to hang the angel on the tree.

Craft:

Trace an angel cookie cutter on a piece of black paper and then cut it out. Fold a piece of white paper in half and then in half again, forming a book. Glue the angel to the front of the white paper. On the inside of the book, write your favorite verse.

Lesson 8: Travel

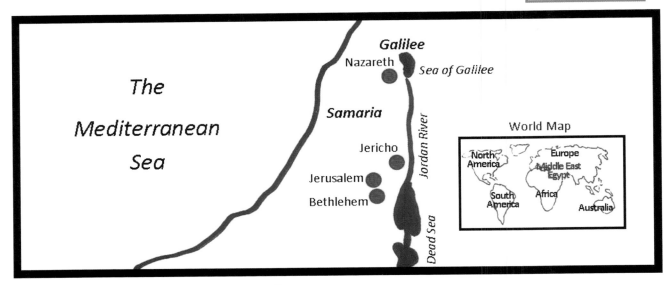

✱ **LABEL the map below:** ✱

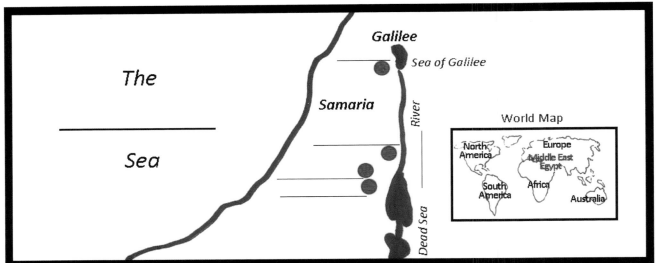

Color the Mediterranean Sea blue and the land brown.

After the lesson:

1.) Draw dashed lines from Galilee to Bethlehem.

2.) Guess how many miles is it from Galilee to Bethlehem?

_____ (As mentioned in the lesson)

Lesson 9: Birth of Jesus

BIBLE LESSONS

You will be coloring and assembling a simple book.

1.) Your teacher will give you one sheet, page 50 from the Teacher Workbook.

2.) Take the page and fold in half and then half again.

3.) This is how the book should look after it is folded with the pages in this order.

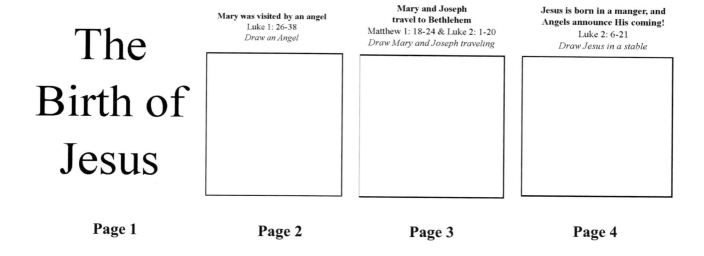

The Birth of Jesus

Mary was visited by an angel
Luke 1: 26-38
Draw an Angel

Mary and Joseph travel to Bethlehem
Matthew 1: 18-24 & Luke 2: 1-20
Draw Mary and Joseph traveling

Jesus is born in a manger, and Angels announce His coming!
Luke 2: 6-21
Draw Jesus in a stable

Page 1   Page 2   Page 3   Page 4

4.) Find and read the scriptures on each page. Draw a picture that explains the scripture.

Lesson 10: The Three Kings

BIBLE LESSONS

Complete below:

We celebrate the Three Wise Men, or Kings, coming on Epiphany, the 12th day after Christmas. Epiphany occurs on January 6th of each year. (The early beginning of a NEW YEAR!)

1.) What is one thing you would like to do differently in the New Year?

_____

_____

2.) Name one activity that you could add as a service to help someone new in the New Year. _____

3.) Name five people you would like to spend more time with in the New Year. _____

_____

4.) Name one thing you can do this year to become closer in your relationship to God. _____

Draw a picture of something you would like to do with your best friend.

Lesson 11: Ash Wednesday and Lent

Personal reflection for Lent, to use in class.

The Lenten Season starts with Ash Wednesday and ends with Easter. Many feel led to give up something during Lent which will help them feel closer to God. Others like to add something to their daily routine to help deepen their relationship with God. Here are some examples of things that you could either give up or add to your daily life.

Give up:

Free time sports, give up the time you spend on sports

Shoes, wear 1 pair of shoes the whole time

Music

Headphones

A certain food you enjoy: chocolate, ice cream, potato chips

Electronics: give up the time you spend on electronic games

Add:

Pray for someone or something new daily

Commit to 10 minutes of Bible reading daily

Become active in an outreach ministry

Find a way to help at least one person a day

Write a positive note to one person daily

Walk for 10 minutes daily in silence and think about what God is trying to say to you

Think about what you would like to give up or add to your daily routine and write it here.

_____

_____

Explain how giving up or adding this item to your daily routine will help you get closer to God.

_____

_____

Write what you will do to accomplish this goal. _____

_____

_____

Lesson 12: Holy Week

Arrange the events in the order they occurred:

A) Judas agrees to betray Jesus for 30 pieces of silver.
B) Jesus dies on the cross.
C) Jesus is judged by Pontius Pilate.
D) Jesus enjoys the Passover meal with his Disciples / The Last Supper
E) Jesus rides into Jerusalem on a donkey / Palm Sunday
F) Jesus is arrested.
G) Jesus and his Disciples go into the garden of Gethsemane to pray.
H) Judas betrays Jesus with a greeting and a kiss.

Hint: If you need help look through Chapters 26 and 27 in the book of Matthew.

1st: _____

2nd:_____

3rd: _____

4th:_____

5th:_____

6th: _____

7th: _____

8th: _____

Craft:

A.) Take a piece of green construction paper and fold it in half.

B.) Cut a 1/2 moon shape on the fold so that when you open it back up it looks like an oval.

C.) Fold the paper back so that it looks like a half moon and cut strips into the paper so that you have leaves. Cut long strips leaving the about 1/2 inch in the center near the fold uncut.

D.) Attach these leaves to an empty paper towel roll or stick.

Lesson 14: Easter

You will be coloring and assembling a simple book.

1.) Your teacher will give you two sheets of paper. Page 74 and 75 from the Teacher Workbook.

2.) Take page 74 with the big words that say "Holly Week & Easter" and fold the paper in half. (The words "Holy Week & Easter should be on the left and the picture labeled "7", with the words "He has RISEN!" should be on the right and they should both be upside down.

3.) Fold in half again. Now, it should have the words, "Holy Week & Easter" on the front with pages 1 and 6 inside. The back should have page 7.

4.) Repeat this for page 75 once you have folded it in half you should have the crown on the left and the image of Jesus praying in the garden on the right.

5.) Fold it half again. Now, it should have page 2 on top and pages 3 and 4 in the middle. The back page should be page 5.

6.) Place the folded page 75 inside of the folded page 74. Staple the book together.

7.) This is how the book should look when done in order.

Lesson 15: Ascension

Jesus was seen!

After the resurrection, Jesus was seen by many. Circle the passage you chose (from the basket provided by your teacher) and then draw and color a picture of how you think it would look.

Matthew 28: 10; Mark 16: 14; Luke 24: 13-16; Luke 24: 33-34; Luke 24:36-43; John 20: 11-18; John 20: 24-29; John 21: 1-14 ; 1 Corinthians 15: 6; 1 Corinthians 15: 7

PROOF!

Lesson 16: Pentecost

Craft:

Gather supplies: 1 piece of red construction paper 2 x 9 inches – base of bookmark, 1 red and 1 yellow piece of construction paper both 2 x 2 inches, glue stick, and scissor.

1.) Write your name on the longer red strip of construction paper.

2.) Cut out the scripture you see below on this page. Then glue it to the center of the red 2 x 9 piece of construction paper.

3.) Cut out the larger flame pattern below. Use it to trace the flame shape on the smaller red piece of 2 x 2 piece of paper and cut out. Glue that to the top of the bookmark.

4.) Cut out the smaller flame pattern below. Use it to trace the flame shape to the yellow piece of paper and cut out.. Glue that to the inside of the red flame.

5.) Decorate more if you have time.

Cut on dotted line, and remove bottom half of worksheet to complete project.

Acts 2: 1-4 The Holy Spirit Comes at Pentecost
When the day of Pentecost came, they were all together in one place. [2] Suddenly a sound like the blowing of a violent wind came from heaven and filled the whole house where they were sitting. [3] They saw what seemed to be tongues of fire that separated and came to rest on each of them. [4] All of them were filled with the Holy Spirit and began to speak in other tongues as the Spirit enabled them.

Large flame

Small flame

Finished Product

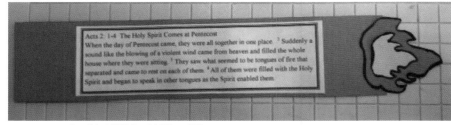

Lesson 17: Mother's Day

Craft: **Make a card for Mother's Day.**

1.) Your teacher will give you a copy of a cup or a pattern to trace, and a piece of colored construction paper folded in half.

2.) Cut out the cup, following the line on the outside of the cup.

3.) Glue the edges of the cut-out teacup (except **DO NOT** glue the top of wide mouth part of the teacup), to the 1/2 sheet of the colored construction paper. If it is easier for you, or if you accidently glue the cup down, you can make a slit that the tea bag can slip into.

Put a tea bag inside the cup as a gift.

Do not glue top or center of cup and slide tea bag in top.

Optional: Glue top but not the center of the cup. Make a slit in the center of the top of the cup and slide tea bag inside.

4.) Slip the individually wrapped tea bag inside the cup.

5.) With a marker or colored pencil; that will show up on the colored paper, write, "A cup of tea from me to you, to thank you for all that you do." Write a personal message and their name, to the person that you love as a mom.

6.) Allow the children time to decorate the teacup.

Lesson 18: Father's Day

BIBLE LESSONS

Craft: Make a gift for Father's Day.

Gather supplies: 2 pieces of the same color construction paper cut in half, glue sticks, stapler, copy of Teacher Workbook pages 91 & 92, and a few markers.

1.) Staple four, half sheets of construction paper together on the left side.

2.) Cut out the image of the "Thumb's Up" on the dotted lines from the image on Teacher Workbook page 91.

3.) Use a glue stick to attach the "Thumb's Up" image to the front cover. Attach the next set of 3 coupons to the 2nd page, and the last set of coupons to the 3rd page.

4.) On the inside of the 4th page write a personal note to the person you consider your Dad and sign it.

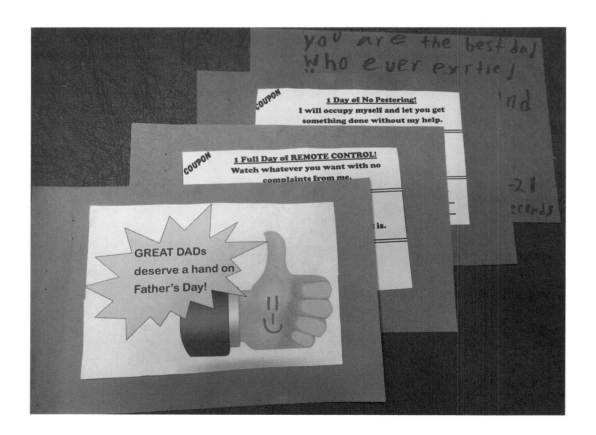

Lesson 19: Famous Children in the Bible

Write in the correct letter of the story that matches the verse(s).

_____1.) Genesis 25: 25-26

_____2.) Genesis 37: 3-4

_____3.) Exodus 2: 1-10

_____4.) 1 Samuel 3: 1-11

_____5.) 1 Samuel 17: 45-50

_____6.) 1 Kings 17: 17-24

_____7.) 2 Kings 11: 21

_____8.) Mark 5: 35-42

_____9.) Luke 2: 46-52

_____10.) John 6: 1-15

A.) Joash, a 7 year old, becomes King

B.) Jewish leader's daughter is raised from the dead

C.) Samuel hears God's voice

D.) Sister of Moses who watched over him in the water

E.) Jacob who held on to his brother Esau's, heel

F.) A boy's lunch feeds 5000 people

G.) Joseph with a colorful coat/robe

H.) Jesus is shown wise beyond his education

I.) David kills Goliath

J.) Elijah brings a boy back to life

Lesson 20: Where Jesus Traveled

BIBLE LESSONS

Use the map below to match the selected events to the location they occurred.

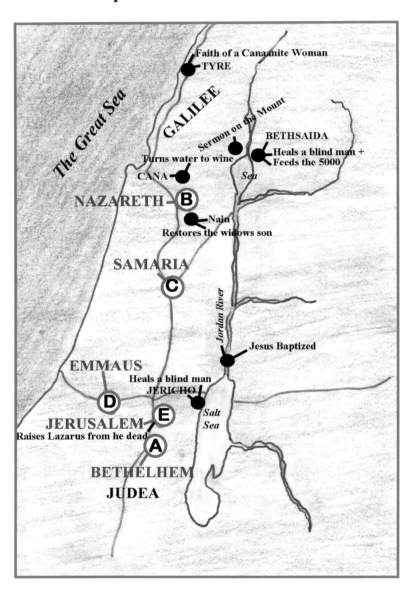

1.) Talks to the woman at the well
John 4: 7-13

2.) Spends His childhood
Matthew 2: 23

3.) Birth
Luke 2: 1-20

4.) Crucified
Matthew 27: 32-34

5.) Appears before two disciples after resurrection
Luke 24: 13-16

A.)_____ (Bethlehem)

B.)_____ (Nazareth)

C.)_____ (Samaria)

D.)_____ (Emmaus)

E.) _____ (Jerusalem-Golgotha)

Lesson 22: Help for Prayers

Craft:

Trace your hand on piece of construction paper.

If you are struggling with how to pray, here's some help!

1.) Trace your hand

2.) Cut it out and glue it onto another piece of construction paper.

3.) Label it as shown.

4.) Practice praying, if you prefer, you can write it down, and read it out loud.

5.) When you get home, hang this somewhere that will remind you to pray. You can pray anytime and anywhere you want.

Prayer is a conversation between you and God. You don't have to use big words or have a script. If you find it hard to pray just remember your hand and follow this guideline.

Lesson 23: Genesis

BIBLE LESSONS

Color/Draw

Day 1 Genesis 1: 3-5 Day and night	**Day 2** Genesis 1: 6-8 Sky	**Day 3** Genesis 1: 9-13 Dry land, plants
Day 4 Genesis 1: 14-19 Sun, moon, and stars	**Day 5** Genesis 1: 20-23 Flying and sea animals	**Day 6** Genesis 1: 24-31 Animals and man

Day 7 Genesis 2: 1-3

God rested

Lesson 24: Exodus

Complete the missing blanks.

The Ten Commandments: Exodus: 20

1.) You shall have no other _____ before me.

2.) You shall not make for yourself an _____ in the form of anything in heaven above or on the earth beneath or in the waters below.

3.) You shall not _____ the name of the Lord your God, for the Lord will not hold anyone guiltless who _____ His name.

4.) Remember the _____ _____ by keeping it holy.

5.) _____ your Father and Mother.

6.) You shall not _____.

7.) You _____ _____ commit adultery.

8.) You _____ _____ steal.

9.) You shall not give false _____ against your neighbor.

10.) You shall not covet your _____ _____. You shall not covet your neighbor's wife, or his male or female servant, his ox or donkey, or anything that belongs to your _____.

Lesson 25: Leviticus & Numbers

What would you do if...?

1.) You found a dollar bill on the floor at the skating rink?

_____

_____

2.) You played with a friend's ball outside and she left without taking it with her?

_____

_____

3.) You accidently wore the wrong jacket home from school?

_____

_____

4.) You go shopping with your parent(s) and realize you didn't get charged for one of your items?

_____

_____

What should your "consequence" be?

1.) You don't tell your parent(s) that you broke something in the house and your brother or sister gets blamed for it.

_____

_____

2.) Your friend comes over to play and brings his Frisbee. You really enjoyed playing with it and you don't have one of your own. He leaves without getting it. You play with it often. He sees you a couple of days later and asks you if he left it at your house. You say, "I can't remember."

_____

_____

Craft:

Take a piece of manila or construction paper and fold it in half, like a card. On the front, write "Thank You!" On the inside, write your parent(s) a note telling them about what you have learned about God from them. Thank them for teaching you about God.

Lesson 27: Joshua, Judges, and Ruth

1.) Who became the leader after Moses died? **Joshua 1: 1 -5**

_____

2.) Joshua sent two spies to Jericho to look for weaknesses in the city. Who helped the two spies? **Joshua 2: 1-4**

_____

3.) Joshua dies in Joshua 24: 29. Who leads the Israelites after Joshua's death? **Judges 2: 16**

_____

4.) Who is a famous female judge? **Judges 4: 4-10**

_____

5.) Who is a famous judge that was strong on the outside but weak on the inside? **Judges 15: 20**

_____

6.) Read **Ruth 1: 6-19**. Why was it unusual for Ruth to be with Naomi?

_____

_____

_____

_____

Lesson 28: 1 Samuel & 2 Samuel

Complete the crossword

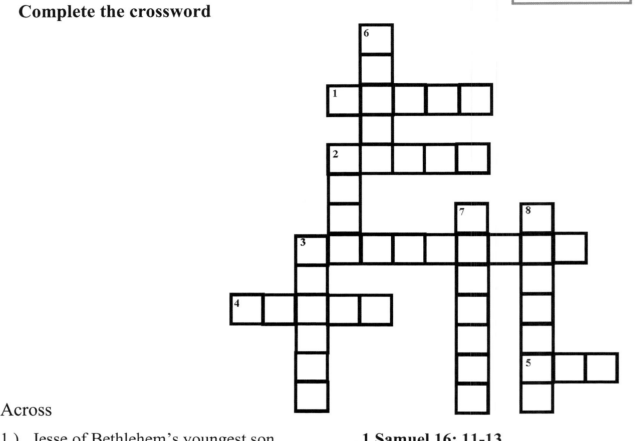

Across

1.) Jesse of Bethlehem's youngest son _____ . **1 Samuel 16: 11-13**

2.) David kills Goliath with a _____ . **1 Samuel 17: 48-49**

3.) Modern name for the weapon used to defeat Goliath? **1 Samuel 17: 50**

4.) Saul put his own _____ on David before he fought Goliath. **1 Samuel 17: 38-40**

5.) How many books of Samuel are there in the Bible? _____

Down

2.) Who is Israel's first King? _____ **1 Samuel 9: 15-17**

3.) Last judge of Israel who anoints Saul _____ **1 Samuel 9: 15-17**

6.) God didn't choose David because of his size but because of his _____. **1 Samuel 16: 7**

7.) David becomes king in 1 Samuel or 2 Samuel? Choose: **1Samuel** or **2Samuel**

8.) A famous Philistine champion _____ . **1 Samuel 17: 4**

Lesson 29: Kings & Chronicles

BIBLE LESSONS

Complete the worksheet the best you can. Draw in extra circles as needed.

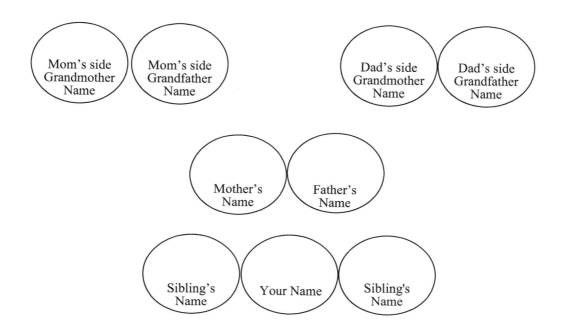

Name the 5 people you like to be with the most.

_____

_____

_____

_____

_____

What do you like most about them?

_____

_____

_____

_____

_____

Consider telling these people how much they mean to you and why. It is always nice to say something positive about someone else and to let them know they are special!

Lesson 30: Ezra, Nehemiah, & Esther

Complete the worksheet the best you can.

Un-jumble these words

RAZE   __ __ __ __ (Book after 2 Chronicles.)
                        5

MEIAHEHN   __ __ __ __ __ __ __ __ (A famous cupbearer mentioned in a book after Ezra.)
                        9

RHETSE   __ __ __ __ __ (Book after Nehemiah.)
                     7

GKNI RCSUY   __ __ __ __ __ __ __ __ __ (King of Persia mentioned in Ezra 1)
                                 6

AJUHD   __ __ __ __ __ (Where Jerusalem is located, Ezra 1:2)
                 3

EURSALJEM   __ __ __ __ __ __ __ __ __ (City where Ezra returned, Ezra 7: 8)
                       2

MELEPT   __ __ __ __ __ __ (The builders laid the foundation for this, read Ezra 3: 10)
            4

DCMRIOEA   __ __ __ __ __ __ __ __ (Raised an orphan like his own daughter, Esther 2: 7)
               1

KGNI EEXXSR   __ __ __ __ __ __ __ __ __ __ (King in Esther 1: 1-3)
                    11

NMAAH   __ __ __ __ __ (Tries to kill Mordecai, Esther 5: 14)
            8

IRESAP   __ __ __ __ __ __ (Esther becomes Queen over this and the land of Media, Esther 1: 3)
            10

NQEEU THSAVI   __ __ __ __ __ __ __ __ __ __ (Esther becomes Queen after her, Esther 1: 9)
                                       12

What we are studying right now! __ __ __ __ __ __ __ __ __ __ __ __
                                             1 2 3   4 5 6 7 8 9 10 11 12

Lesson 31: Job

Find the following words:

Job, Psalms, Proverbs, Ecclesiastes, Solomon, Songs, and David

E	E	N	L	K	M	O	N	T	F	J	G
D	C	J	H	R	D	A	V	I	D	G	T
S	G	C	F	J	E	N	U	S	O	N	E
P	O	K	L	H	P	S	G	M	P	O	S
R	I	N	M	E	V	O	P	L	W	M	K
O	D	Q	G	O	S	B	I	K	S	O	S
V	F	L	O	S	T	I	D	E	T	L	I
E	Q	C	N	B	D	S	A	H	Q	O	D
R	C	G	O	R	R	M	T	S	U	S	R
B	M	J	R	G	J	L	N	S	T	H	M
S	E	O	S	M	L	A	S	P	R	E	N
L	N	H	P	K	O	G	I	T	F	T	S

Answer below:

1.) What are the 3 worst things that ever happened to you? Think about them but do not write them down.

2.) Write below the 3 best things that ever happened to you.

_____

_____

_____

Lesson 32: Psalms

Types of Psalms:

- **Anger:** Requests that God punish evil people
- **Confession:** Shows us how to tell God about our sins
- **Worship:** Used on special holidays and in groups
- **History:** Tells what God has done
- **Praise:** Thanks God for all he has done
- **Friendship:** Reminds us that God loves us
- **Messiah:** Tells about Jesus

Match the type of Psalm with the definition:

1.) Anger _____   A. Thanks God for all he has done
2.) Confession _____   B. Tells what God has done
3.) Worship _____   C. Reminds us that God loves us
4.) History _____   D. Requests that God punishes evil people
5.) Praise _____   E. Shows us how to tell God about our sins
6.) Friendship _____   F. Tells about Jesus
7.) Messiah _____   G. Used on special holidays and in groups

Which type of Psalms are these?
Praise, History, Friendship, Anger, Confession, Messiah, Worship
Circle One

1.) Psalm 23: 6 <u>Friendship</u> or <u>Worship</u>?

2.) Psalm 33: 1 <u>History</u> or <u>Praise</u>?

3.) Psalm 35: 19 <u>Friendship</u> or <u>Anger</u>?

4.) Psalm 51: 3-4 <u>Confession</u> or <u>History</u>?

5.) Psalm 89: 8 <u>History</u> or <u>Messiah</u>?

6.) Psalm 106: 7 <u>History</u> or <u>Worship</u>?

7.) Psalm 122: 4 <u>Confession</u> or <u>Worship</u>?

Craft:

Fold a piece of construction paper in half to make a card. Decorate it and inside it write a thank-you note to someone you are thankful for.

Lesson 33: Proverbs

Circle the best answer:

1A.) You are worried about a book report coming up. You are working on it and it's coming together, but it's the first book report you've ever done. You pray to God to give you peace and understanding.

1B.) You are worried about a book report. You voice your concerns to your friends, family, and anyone who will listen. You put off doing it because you are sure you will fail before you even start.

2A.) Your family plants a garden and you have lots of vegetables. It's your responsibility to water the garden and harvest the vegetables. Everyday you collect the ones that are ready and you even give some away to family and friends.

2B.) Your family plants a garden and you have lots vegetables. It's your responsibility to water the garden and harvest the vegetables. You get busy playing with both friends and video games. You forget to water the garden and the few vegetables that do grow are small. You harvest very little.

3A.) A friend (Tom) tells you that (Sally) is struggling with math. Tom tells you that on Sally's last test she only scored 40 out of 100. You both laugh. You tell another friend (David) about how poorly Sally is doing in math. When the teacher calls on Sally to answer a question in class everyone starts laughing. Somebody whispers "Sally doesn't know the answer."

3B.) A friend (Tom) tells you that (Sally) is struggling with math. Tom tells you that on Sally's last test she only scored 40 out of 100. Tom laughs and says Sally is dumb. You tell Tom that it's not nice to talk bad about people. Privately you go to Sally and ask Sally if she wants to ask her mom if she can come over and do math homework together.

4A.) Sally found out that Tom was telling everyone about her bad grades in math. She was really hurt. She thought about getting revenge by telling some secrets about Tom that she knew would hurt Tom. After thinking about it, she decided to forgive Tom and just ignore it. In a couple of days she took a math test. She scored a 95. It was the second highest grade in the class. The teacher complimented Sally on how well she improved in front of the whole class.

4B.) Sally found out Tom was telling everyone about her bad grades in math. She told everyone about how he got a D in Art last year because he didn't complete a project. The two said hateful things about each other for weeks. Their friends couldn't stand being around either of them anymore. Both Sally and Tom found themselves sitting alone at lunch.

Craft:

Your teacher will give you a leaf. Write one thing you are thankful for on the leaf. Write your name on the leaf as well. Color the leaf and display it on the poster your teacher made for the class.

Lesson 35: Isaiah, Jeremiah, Lamentations, & Ezekiel

Complete the answers below.

1.) Surely this is our God; we _____ in him and he saved us. **(Isaiah 25: 9)**

2.) In **Isaiah 56: 10-11,** The Lord compares the prophets / watchmen to what? _____

3.) Ask where the good way is, and _____ in it, and you will find rest for your souls. **(Jeremiah 6: 16)**

4.) Can you hide from God? **Jeremiah 23: 23-24** _____

5.) Read **Lamentations 1: 1,** is it happy or sad? _____

6.) The Lord is _____ to those whose _____ is in him, to the one who seeks him; it is _____ to wait quietly for the salvation of the Lord. **(Lamentations 3: 25-26)**

7.) They stood on the walls of a city and warned people of danger. **(Ezekiel 3: 16-21)** _____

8.) I will give you a new _____ and put a new _____ in you; I will remove from you your _____ of stone and give you a _____ of flesh. **(Ezekiel 36: 26)**

Lesson 36: Daniel, Hosea, Joel, & Amos

BIBLE LESSONS

Complete the answers below.

1.) Write the names of Daniel's three friends _____ , _____ , _____ . **(Daniel 3: 12)**

2.) Why did Daniel and his three friends get thrown into the fiery furnace? _____ **(Daniel 3: 12)**

3.) Why did King Darius put Daniel in the lions den? _____ _____ _____

(Daniel 6: 6-9)

4.) Was Daniel hurt by the lions? Yes or No? _____ **(Daniel 6: 21-22)**

5.) "I led them with cords of human _____, with ties of love. **(Hosea 11: 4)**

6.) Who said "I am sending you grain, new wine and olive oil, enough to satisfy you fully; ..." **(Joel 2: 19)** _____

7.) "Seek good, _____ _____, that you may live. Then the Lord God Almighty will be with you, ..."**(Amos 5: 14)**

8.) Is it okay to treat the poor as if they aren't as important? Yes or No? _____ **(Amos 8: 4-6)**

Complete the answers below.

Anagram:

Word list: Punish, Obadiah, Repent, Whale, Jonah, Micah, Nahum, Habakkuk, Nineveh, Fish, Swallowed, Storm

1.) LAHWE: _____

2.) HNAUM: _____

3.) ROSTM: _____

4.) DAOIBHA: _____

5.) AICHM: _____

6.) KAKBAHKU: _____

7.) VIENHEN: _____

8.) HIFS: _____

9.) LOWSALEWD: _____

10.) HISNUP: _____

11.) NOJAH: _____

12.) TERPEN: _____

Lesson 38: Zephaniah, Haggai, Zechariah, & Malachi

Break the Code.

Circle the correct answer. Write the corresponding letter below in the blanks provided.

1.) A friend drops all their books …
H: You stop and help them pick them up.
E: You keep walking and ignore them.

2.) Someone you don't know is eating alone at lunch...
A: You introduce yourself and offer to sit with them.
O: You sit with your best friend that you love to talk to.

3.) You are on a soccer team and your teammate causes your team to lose a point...
D: You groan really loud and kick the ground.
F: You tell them it's okay and tell them they will make the point next time!

4.) Your brother is being quiet and looks sad…
N: You go play a video game in the other room.
L: You ask him why he looks sad and offer to listen.

5.) You see someone stealing…
T: You tell your parents.
G: You act like you didn't see it.

6.) You are at a friend's house and accidently break his toy, but he doesn't see you...
M: You blame his sister.
F: You admit you broke it and offer to replace it.

7.) A friend comes over to watch TV, both of your favorite shows are playing…
R: You watch your show because it's your house.
I: You watch their show because they are your guest.

8.) Your sister leaves her coat in the movie theater…
U: You offer to go back and help her find it.
S: You complain that she always forgets everything.

___ ___ ___ ___ ___ ___ ___ ___
 3   2   7   5   1   6   8   4

Lesson 39: Matthew, Part 1

Read **Matthew 18: 21-35**

Draw a picture of a man in jail, who owed a lot of money.

The man begged for forgiveness and for time to repay the loan. His debt was forgiven.

On the next squares, draw a picture of a free man, who runs into someone that owes him a smaller amount of money. Refer back to the scripture above.

Draw a picture of what <u>SHOULD</u> have happened.   Draw a picture of what <u>REALLY</u> happened.

What happened to the man who didn't forgive like he was forgiven? _____

_____

_____

Lesson 40: Matthew, Part 2

Draw a picture of a drawbridge that goes to a kingdom. Now on the lower side; at ground level, draw a very small entrance. This entrance was so small that one person could barely get through it. When the draw bridge or main entrance to a kingdom or large city was closed, this small entrance was used in emergencies. Read **Matthew 19: 24**, when the scripture mentions the "eye of a needle" it may have been referring to this small door that was used for emergency passage.

Lesson 41: Mark

Many of the parables, miracles, and teaching of Jesus are mentioned in different parts of the Gospels. Below is a chart with a few of them mentioned.

Title	Type	Matthew	Mark	Luke	John
Calms the storm	Miracle	8: 23-37	4: 35-41		
Faith of the Centurion	Miracle	8: 5-13		4: 39-39	
Feeds the 5000	Miracle	14: 1-21	6: 30-44	9: 12-17	6: 5-15
Paralyzed man	Miracle	9: 1-8	2: 1-12	5: 17-26	
Peter's Mother-in-law	Miracle	8: 14-17	1: 29-31	4: 38-39	
Walks on water	Miracle	14: 22-23	6: 45-52		6: 16-21
Give to Caesar	Teaching		12: 13-17		
Sowing of the seeds	Parable	13: 1-8, 18-23	4: 3-8, 14-20	9: 5-8, 11-15	
Mustard Seed	Parable	13: 31-32, 17: 20			
Weeds with the wheat	Parable	13: 24-39, 13: 36-39			

Using the chart above answer the questions below.

1.) Which **miracle** is mentioned in all 4 of the gospels? _____

2.) How many **miracles** are mentioned 3 times in the gospels? _____

3.) Write the title or name of the **parable** written 3 times in the gospels? _____

4.) Write the name of the book of the Bible that is **teaching** about giving to Caesar.

_____

5.) Which two **miracles** were mentioned in the book of John? _____

_____

6.) The **miracle** concerning the faith of the centurion that was mentioned in which 2 books?

_____

7.) In which book were the **parables** of the mustard seed and weeds mentioned? _____

8.) Write the books, chapters, and verses of the **miracle** of Jesus walking on water. _____

_____

Lesson 42: Luke

Read the verses below and match them with the **miracle**.

These are not all the miracles mentioned in the book of Luke.

1.) Luke 4: 38-39 _____   A. Man with leprosy

2.) Luke 5: 1-11 _____   B. Centurion's servant

3.) Luke 5: 12-14 _____   C. Peter's Mother-in-law

4.) Luke 5: 17-26 _____   D. Paralyzed man

5.) Luke 6: 6-11 _____   E. Man with shriveled hand

6.) Luke 7: 1-10 _____   F. Woman with bleeding

7.) Luke 7: 11-15 _____   G. Calming of the storm

8.) Luke 8: 22-25 _____   H. Feeding the 5000

9.) Luke 9: 12-17 _____   I. Huge catch of fish

10.) Luke 13: 11-13 _____   J. Widow's son at Nain

Read the verses below and match them with the **parable**.

These are not all of the parables mentioned in the book of Luke.

11.) Luke 7: 41-43 _____   A. Canceled debts

12.) Luke 8: 5-8 _____   B. Cost of discipleship

13.) Luke 10: 30-37 _____   C. Fig tree

14.) Luke 13: 6-9 _____   D. Good Samaritan

15.) Luke 14: 28-33 _____   E. Lost coin

16.) Luke 15: 3-7 _____   F. Lost sheep

17.) Luke 15: 8-10 _____   G. Lost son

18.) Luke 15: 11-32 _____   H. Persistent Widow

19.) Luke 18: 1-8 _____   I. Sower

20.) Luke 21: 29-31 _____   J. Unfruitful fig tree

Lesson 43: John

Complete below:

Do you believe in miracles? Do miracles still happen today?

1.) Write down 5 times you had a prayer answered.

_____

_____

_____

_____

_____

2.) God's spirit works through us everyday. Sometimes you feel like you should do something but you don't know why. You may feel the need to call someone. You may feel like you need to do something nice for someone in particular. Sometimes this is God "telling" you to do something nice. Write about a time you felt like God was "nudging" you to do something.

_____

_____

_____

_____

_____

3.) When you get home today, ask your parents or favorite adult to tell you about a time that they witnessed a miracle. If they can't think of one right away, have them think about a time when they had a feeling they needed to do something and when they finally did it they realized it was God telling them to do so. Start a journal to record these things as they happen to you in your life.

Lesson 44: Acts, Part 1

Directions for planting your seed.

You will need 2 small disposable coffee cups, a dull pencil, 1/2 cup of soil, water, and a seed.

1.) Use the dull pencil to make 3 small holes in the bottom of one disposable coffee cup.

2.) Fill the cup with approximately 1/4 cup of soil.

3.) Place the seed on top of the soil and cover it with remaining soil.

4.) Set this cup inside the other cup. Pour a small amount of water into the cup that has the seed. The water will drain through the holes into the empty cup below. Write your name on outside of cup and set it on the window sill until time to leave.

Today we will be learning about the book of Acts. We have learned a lot about the Bible and God this year. Thankfully, God is very patient with us as we are learning. Just like God is patient and caring with us, we need to be patient and caring with this seed. We need to water it and make sure it has sunlight to grow. We need the Bible and relationships with other Christians so that we may grow. Take care of this plant and show God's love toward it so it can be big and strong one day.

Lesson 45: Acts, Part 2

Find and read Acts 28: 1-10. Complete the below.

1.) Paul was shipwrecked on the island of _____.

2.) A _____ bit Paul on the hand.

3.) Paul should have _____ from the bite.

4.) The people thought Paul was a _____ because he did not get sick.

5.) Paul _____ many people that were sick.

Draw a picture of this story.

Lesson 46: Romans

Make a scroll.

Gather supplies: Tan paper (either construction or butcher paper), two pencils, scotch tape, glue stick, two straws, small amount of ribbon, your favorite scripture from below.

1.) Cut the paper so that it is as long as your straws in height (usually about 8 inches). Make sure your paper is at least 9-12 inches long for a regular sized straw.

2.) Wrinkle the paper repeatedly by balling it up and then straightening it out. Make sure you are fairly gentle so that you do not tear the paper.

3.) Gently roll the two shorter sides of the paper around your pencils. You can use a small amount of tape to temporarily hold the paper in place. This is to curl the paper. Unroll it and replace the pencils with the straws permanently. When adding the straws you may add more tape.

4.) Unroll the scroll and use the glue stick to glue your favorite verse from below to the center.

5.) Reroll your scroll and tie the ribbon around it to secure it.

Choose one below:

Romans 3: 21-24 Righteousness Through Faith
[21] But now apart from the law the righteousness of God has been made known, to which the Law and the Prophets testify.[22] This righteousness is given through faith in Jesus Christ to all who believe. There is no difference between Jew and Gentile,[23] for all have sinned and fall short of the glory of God, [24] and all are justified freely by His grace through the redemption that came by Christ Jesus.

Romans 8: 28 In all things God works for Good
[28] And we know that in all things God works for the good of those who love Him, who have been called according to His purpose.

Romans 12: 12-13 Love in Action
[12] Be joyful in hope, patient in affliction, faithful in prayer. [13] Share with the Lord's people who are in need. Practice hospitality.

Lesson 47: Corinthians

Fill in the blank with the matching letter.

Love is patient  **A**	Love is not easily angered.  **B**	Love always trusts.  **C**
Love is kind.  **D**	Love does not boast.  **E**	Love rejoices in the truth.  **F**
Love keeps no record of wrongs.  **G**	Faith, Hope, and Love.  **H**	Love is not jealous or envious.  **I**

The answers below come from verses 4, 5, 6, 7, and 13, found in 1 Corinthians 13.

1.) [4] Love is patient, _____. It does not envy, it does not boast, it is not proud.

2.) [5] It does not dishonor others, it is not self-seeking, _____, it keeps no record of wrongs.

3.) [13] And now these three remain: _____. But the greatest of these is love.

4.) [4] Love is patient, love is kind. It does not envy, _____, it is not proud.

5.) [6] Love does not delight in evil but _____.

6.) [4] _____, love is kind. It does not envy, it does not boast, it is not proud.

7.) [7] It always protects, _____, always hopes, always perseveres.

8.) [5] It does not dishonor others, it is not self-seeking, it is not easily angered, it _____.

9.) [4] Love is patient, love is kind. _____ it does not boast, it is not proud.

Design your own flag for each "Fruits of the Spirit."

*Forbearance means someone who is patient

LOVE

JOY

PEACE

FORBEARANCE

KINDNESS

GOODNESS

FAITHFULNESS

GENTLENESS

SELF CONTROL

Lesson 49: Thessalonians & Timothy

Write to a pen pal. Pen Pals are friends that you send letters or emails to. In today's lesson, your teacher has chosen someone special for you to write to. Use the space below to tell them a little about yourself and ask them questions to learn more about them. Think about doing this once a month at home with your family.

Lesson 50: Titus, Philemon, & Hebrews

Faith by Action.

Hebrews 11: 1 "Now faith is confidence in what we hope for and assurance about what we do not see."

In the following scenarios write a "T" for True if the scenario showed faith or write a "F" for False it they did not have faith.

_____1.) Noah builds a large Ark / Boat after being warned by God of the flood.

_____2.) A person saves all his money and only buys necessities, never shares with anyone.

_____3.) Thomas asks to touch Jesus side so that he could believe it was Him.

_____4.) A little boy named David kills a giant with only a stone.

_____5.) Job's friends said he was being punished for doing something wrong, even though he was confident that he had not.

_____6.) Zechariah laughed when an angel told him that in his old age he would have a son.

_____7.) Mary said "May your word to me be fulfilled," when she was told that she would conceive and give birth to a son, who would be named Jesus.

_____8.) Peter starts to walk on water after Jesus calls to him, but then falls.

_____9.) A woman touches Jesus' cloak and is healed.

_____10.) Moses raised his staff and stretched out his hand over the sea, and the Red Sea was parted. He and the rest of the Israelites crossed on dry land.

Lesson 51: James & Peter

Color the sheet below and answer the 3 questions.

Write or draw 10 positive words.

James 3: 5-6

[5] Likewise, the tongue is a small part of the body, but it makes great boasts. Consider what a great forest is set on fire by a small spark.[6] The tongue also is a fire, a world of evil among the parts of the body. It corrupts the whole body, sets the whole course of one's life on fire, and is itself set on fire by hell.

1.) Can the tongue be used for good? Yes or No

2.) Can the tongue be used for bad? Yes or No

James 3: 9-12

[9] With the tongue we praise our Lord and Father, and with it we curse human beings, who have been made in God's likeness. [10] Out of the same mouth come praise and cursing. My brothers and sisters, this should not be. [11] Can both fresh water and salt water flow from the same spring? [12] My brothers and sisters, can a fig tree bear olives, or a grapevine bear figs? Neither can a salt spring produce fresh water.

3.) How can we be more careful with what we say? _____

_____

_____

Use the sign language symbols below to read the Bible verse from 2 John.

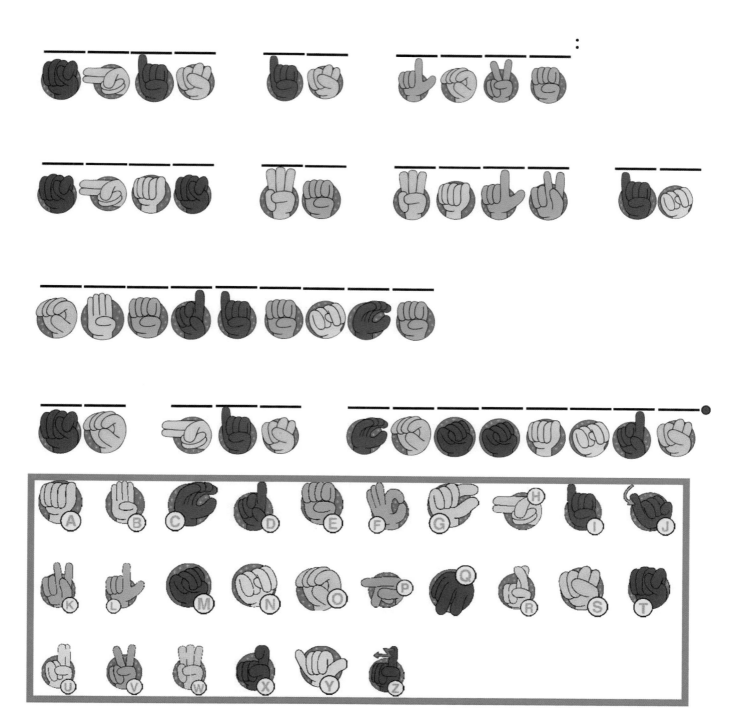

Use the Morse code symbols below to read the Bible verse from Revelation Chapter 19.

BLESSED ARE

THOSE WHO ARE

INVITED TO THE

WEDDING SUPPER

OF THE LAMB

A $\bullet-$	J $\bullet---$	S $\bullet\bullet\bullet$
B $-\bullet\bullet\bullet$	K $-\bullet-$	T $-$
C $-\bullet-\bullet$	L $\bullet-\bullet\bullet$	U $\bullet\bullet-$
D $-\bullet\bullet$	M $--$	V $\bullet\bullet\bullet-$
E $\bullet$	N $-\bullet$	W $\bullet--$
F $\bullet\bullet-\bullet$	O $---$	X $-\bullet\bullet-$
G $--\bullet$	P $\bullet--\bullet$	Y $-\bullet--$
H $\bullet\bullet\bullet\bullet$	Q $--\bullet-$	Z $--\bullet\bullet$
I $\bullet\bullet$	R $\bullet-\bullet$	

Printed in Great Britain
by Amazon

30246649R00037